A Treasury
of Four-Hand
Piano Music

EDITED BY

RUTH WATANABE

THE SCRIBNER LIBRARY OF PIANO MUSIC

CHARLES SCRIBNER'S SONS · NEW YORK

Introduction

TO make music with someone is one of the greatest rewards of a pianist. Not only is it an enjoyable discipline, contributing to a fine sense of ensemble and mutual cooperation among players, but a profitable pastime as well. Included in this volume are piano duets at various levels of pianistic development and encompassing various styles and forms of the classic and romantic periods. They may be played by pupil and teacher or by two students. Because the duet is the logical introduction of the young pianist to chamber music, these pieces may be used to add another dimension to a private music lesson or to a class. Moreover, most of the compositions are suitable for recital, and some of the more advanced works are of concert caliber, both technically and musically. Thus, this volume is offered as an opportunity to enjoy the pleasures of "Four-Hand Piano Music."

RUTH WATANABE

Preface

THE piano has been called the most "lonesome" of instruments because a great part of its repertory is for solo performance. It is often pointed out that players of string instruments, of woodwind, brass, and percussion instruments, have the opportunity of playing with others in orchestras, bands, and various ensemble groups, an experience which is denied pianists.

But this is not really true. While the piano is essentially a "solo" instrument it is also a magnificent ensemble instrument, whether it appears as the solo instrument with a symphony orchestra, in chamber music, as an accompaniment for other solo instruments or voice, or as part of a piano ensemble.

There is nothing more exciting, or exacting, than a two-piano performance. There is no better way of becoming intimately acquainted with symphonic literature than through arrangements for two pianos— eight-hands or four-hands — or for piano duet. Indeed, many of us received our first introduction to the great symphonies in this manner.

However, since two pianos are not always readily available, especially in the home, the most effective and practical ensemble experience is found in the piano duet. To assist in developing this kind of ensemble technique, Dr. Watanabe has prepared a fascinating volume entitled *A Treasury of Four-Hand Piano Music*, and consisting entirely of compositions written for piano four-hands.

The list extends from the period of Mozart, Schubert, and Beethoven, to the works of such twentieth century composers as Ernst von Dohnányi and Paul Juon. In between will be found many charming waltzes, compositions in other dance forms, and other works in a variety of styles and forms.

The volume brings not only a new musical experience to the student; it is also fun to play.

HOWARD HANSON

Preface excerpted from Volume 6 of *The New Scribner Music Library*, Howard Hanson, Editor-in-Chief.

Contents

List of Titles

Waltz
Op. 66 No. 7

Secondo

Anton Arensky
(1861-1906)

Allegro non troppo

Un poco più vivo

Waltz
Op. 66 No. 7

Primo

Anton Arensky
(1861-1906)

Allegro non troppo

Un poco più vivo

Secondo

Secondo

Secondo

Secondo

Tempo I

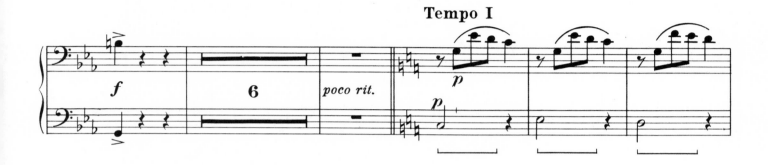

Un poco più vivo

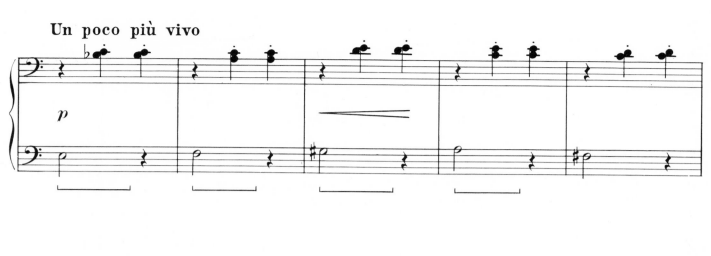

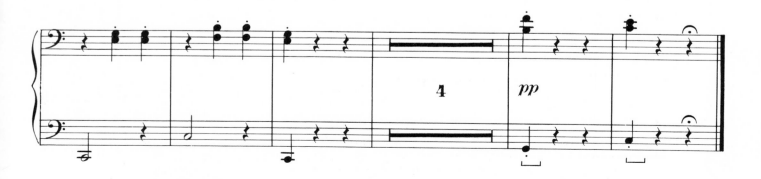

Sonata in D Major
Op. 6

Secondo

Ludwig van Beethoven
(1770-1827)

Sonata in D Major

Op. 6

Primo

Ludwig van Beethoven
(1770-1827)

Secondo

Secondo

Secondo

Moderato

Secondo

Secondo

Secondo

Primo

Sonatina in F Major

Secondo

Ludwig van Beethoven

Sonatina in F Major

Primo

Ludwig van Beethoven

Allegro assai

Secondo

Secondo

Rondo
Allegro

42

Secondo

TWO LOVE SONG WALTZES
1. In Woods Embower'd
Op. 52a   No. 9

In woods embower'd,'neath azure sky,
A rosy maid looks from window high.
Well-guarded is she with lock and key:

With ten iron bars is her doorway made fast.
"Ha! ten iron bars are a jest to me;
As though they were glass, they shall shatter'd be."

Secondo

Johannes Brahms
(1833 - 1897)

TWO LOVE SONG WALTZES
1. In Woods Embower'd
Op. 52a No. 9

In woods embower'd, 'neath azure sky,
A rosy maid looks from window high.
Well guarded is she with lock and key:

With ten iron bars is her doorway made fast.
"Ha! ten iron bars are a jest to me;
As though they were glass, they shall shatter'd be."

Primo

Johannes Brahms
(1833 - 1897)

Secondo

2. No, There Is No Bearing with Them

Op. 52a No. 11

No, there is no bearing with
these spiteful neighbors:
All they do is misconstrue
each other's labors.

Am I merry? then by
evil thoughts I'm haunted;
Am I sad? they say I
am with love demented.

2. No, There Is No Bearing with Them

Op. 52a No. 11

No, there is no bearing with
these spiteful neighbors:
All they do is misconstrue
each other's labors.

Am I merry? then by
evil thoughts I'm haunted;
Am I sad? they say I
am with love demented.

FIVE MELODIOUS PIECES

Secondo

1. Allegretto
Op. 149 No. 9

Anton Diabelli
(1781 - 1858)

FIVE MELODIOUS PIECES

Primo

1. Allegretto

Op. 149 No. 9

Anton Diabelli
(1781 - 1858)

Secondo

2. Allegro

Op. 149 No. 10

2. Allegro

Op. 149 No. 10

3. Romance
Op. 149 No. 11

4. Andante
Op. 149 No. 12

3. Romance
Op. 149 No. 11

4. Andante
Op. 149 No. 12

Secondo

5. Allegro

Op. 149 No. 13

5. Allegro

Op. 149   No. 13

Waltz
Op. 3
Secondo

Ernst von Dohnányi
(1877 - 1960)

Waltz
Op. 3

Primo

Ernst von Dohnányi
(1877 - 1960)

Allegro risoluto

Secondo

Secondo

(sopra)
cross hands
with Secondo

Secondo

Secondo

Kitty-Valse

Op. 56 No. 4

Secondo

Gabriel Fauré
(1845-1924)

Kitty-Valse

Op.56 No. 4

Primo

Gabriel Fauré
(1845-1924)

Secondo

senza Ped.

Secondo

Secondo

Secondo

Norwegian Dance
Op. 35 No. 2

Secondo

Edvard Grieg
(1843-1907)

Norwegian Dance

Op. 35 No. 2

Primo

Edvard Grieg
(1843-1907)

Primo

Forest Bird
Op. 43 No. 3

Secondo

Adolf Jensen
(1837-1879)

Forest Bird
Op. 43 No. 3

Primo

Adolf Jensen
(1837-1879)

Secondo

Dance Rhythms
Op. 14 No. 1
Secondo

Paul Juon
(1872-1940)

Dance Rhythms
Op. 14 No. 1

Primo

Paul Juon
(1872-1940)

Dance Rhythms
Op. 14 No. 4

Secondo

Paul Juon

Dance Rhythms
Op. 14 No. 4

Primo

Paul Juon

Secondo

Theme and Variations
Op. 62 No. 10

Secondo

Richard Kleinmichel
(1846-1901)

Theme and Variations
Op. 62 No. 10

Primo

Richard Kleinmichel
(1846-1901)

Secondo

Var. II

mf

Var. III
Più lento

p dolce

cresc.

pp

poco rit.

sf

Var. II

Var. III
Più lento

Var. IV

Poco animato

Var. IV

Poco animato

The Wanderer

Secondo

Louis Köhler
(1820-1886)

The Wanderer

Primo

Louis Köhler
(1820-1886)

Secondo

Minuet

from Op. 44, No. 3

Secondo

Friedrich Kuhlau
(1786-1832)

Minuet

from Op. 44, No. 3

Primo

Friedrich Kuhlau
(1786-1832)

108

Secondo

Minuet D. C. without repeats

Minuet D. C. without repeats

Allegro Brillant
Op. 92

Secondo

Felix Mendelssohn
(1809 - 1847)

Allegro assai vivace

Allegro Brillant

Op. 92

Primo

Felix Mendelssohn
(1809 - 1847)

Secondo

Secondo

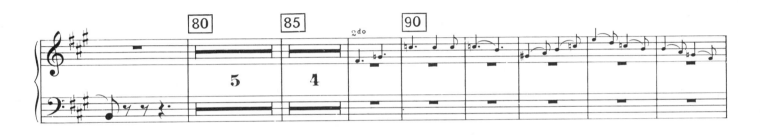

Secondo

Primo

Secondo

Secondo

Secondo

Secondo

Secondo

Secondo

Secondo

Secondo

Bolero
Op. 12 No. 5
Secondo

Moritz Moszkowski
(1854-1925)

Con spirito

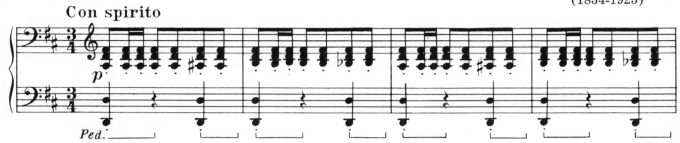

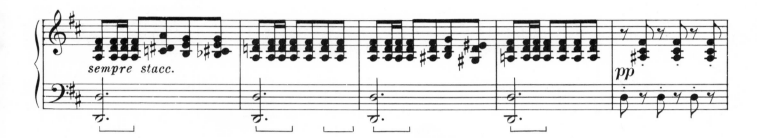

Bolero
Op. 12 No. 5

Primo

Moritz Moszkowski
(1854-1925)

Secondo

Secondo

Spanish Dance
Op. 12 No. 1

Secondo

Allegro brioso

Moritz Moszkowski

Spanish Dance
Op. 12 No. 1

Primo

Moritz Moszkowski

Secondo

Secondo

Sonata in B-flat Major

K. 358

Secondo

Wolfgang Amadeus Mozart
(1756-1791)

Sonata in B-flat Major
K. 358

Primo

Wolfgang Amadeus Mozart
(1756-1791)

Secondo

Secondo

Primo

Secondo

Secondo

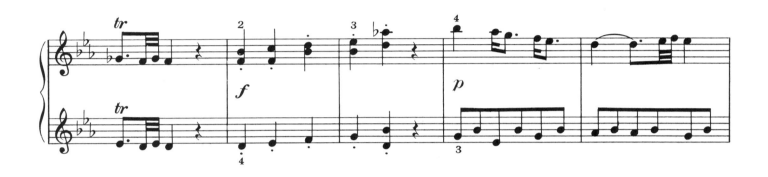

Secondo

Secondo

Molto presto

Molto presto

Secondo

Secondo

Polish Dance

from the *Tatra Album*

Op. 12 No. 1

Secondo

Ignace Paderewski
(1860 - 1941)

Polish Dance
from the *Tatra Album*
Op. 12 No. 1

Primo

Ignace Paderewski
(1860 - 1941)

Allegro con brio

Secondo

Secondo

Primo

Secondo

Secondo

H Poco più mosso

Barcarolle

Secondo

Eduard Poldini
(1869-1957)

Barcarolle

Primo

Eduard Poldini
(1869-1957)

Secondo

Secondo

Primo

Gavotte
Secondo

Eduard Poldini

Allegro moderato

Gavotte
Primo

Eduard Poldini

TWO DANCES
from *Petite Suite*
1. Tarantella
Op. 30 No. 3

Secondo

Vladimir Rebikov
(1866 - 1920)

TWO DANCES
from *Petite Suite*
1. Tarantella
Op. 30 No. 3

Vladimir Rebikov
(1866 - 1920)

Primo

* keep hand low; *Secondo* will play a B - flat above the *Primo* part in the next measure.

Secondo

Secondo

2. Waltz

Op. 30 No. 1

Secondo

2. Waltz

Op. 30 No. 1

Primo

206

Secondo

Secondo

210

Secondo

Secondo

Love's Happiness

Op. 165 No. 7

Secondo

Carl Reinecke
(1824 - 1910)

Love's Happiness

Op. 165 No. 7

Primo

Carl Reinecke
(1824 - 1910)

Secondo

Primo

Rustic Dance

Op. 122b No. 6

Secondo

Carl Reinecke

Rustic Dance

Op. 122b No. 6

Primo

Tempo di Valzer, lento

Carl Reinecke

From Oesterle's *Graded Four-Hand Collection*, copyright 1910 by G. Schirmer, Inc., reprinted by permission.

Secondo

Album Leaf
Op. 81

Secondo

Camille Saint-Saëns
(1835-1921)

Album Leaf
Op. 81

Primo

Camille Saint-Saëns
(1835 - 1921)

Andantino quasi allegretto

Secondo

Polonaise
Op. 61   No. 1

Secondo

Franz Schubert
(1797-1828)

Polonaise
Op. 61 No. 1

Primo

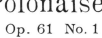

Franz Schubert
(1797-1828)

Fine

Secondo

Trio

Polonaise da Capo

Primo

Polonaise da Capo

Three Souvenir Waltzes
Op. 64

1

Secondo

Eduard Schütt
(1856 - 1933)

Three Souvenir Waltzes

Op. 64

1

Primo

Eduard Schütt
(1856 - 1933)

Secondo

Secondo

2

Moderato un poco moto

2

Moderato un poco moto

3

3

Secondo

Birthday March
Op. 85 No. 1

Secondo

Robert Schumann
(1810 - 1856)

* Pedal is marked for both parts. Either secondo or primo may pedal.

From Oesterle's *Graded Four-Hand Collection*, copyright 1910 by G. Schirmer, Inc., reprinted by permission.

Birthday March
Op. 85 No. 1

Primo

Robert Schumann
(1810-1856)

* Pedal is marked for both parts. Either secondo or primo may pedal.

Secondo

Waltz
Op. 59 No. 2

Secondo

Christian Sinding
(1856-1941)

Waltz
Op. 59 No. 2

Primo

Christian Sinding
(1856-1941)

Secondo

Secondo

Adagio
Op. 10 No. 5

Secondo

Carl Maria von Weber
(1786 - 1826)

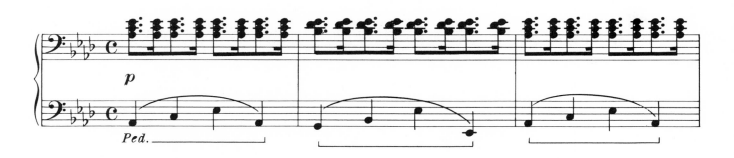

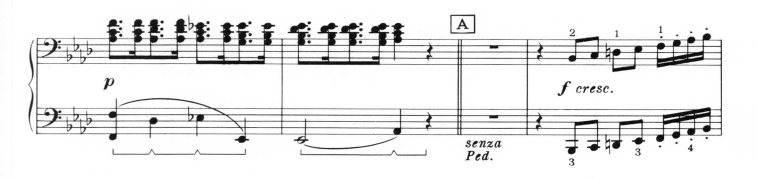

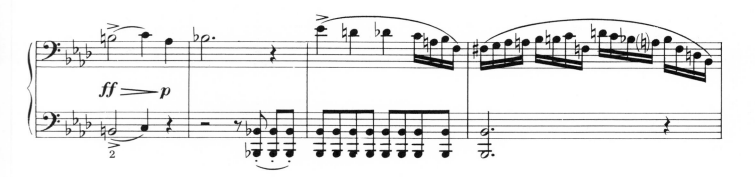

Adagio

Op. 10 No. 5

Primo

Carl Maria von Weber
(1786 - 1826)

Secondo